Out of this World

TROUBLE ON NOVA

Contents

by Sally Odgers
illustrated by Matt Lin

S P A C E ... P O R T S

Reading Manga: What is it?

The Japanese word 'manga' has been used for nearly 200 years. It means whimsical pictures (man = whimsical, ga = pictures).

Today, manga is a label for Japanese-style graphic novels, comic books and animated movies (also called anime). What's the difference between a graphic novel and a comic book? The answer is in your hands. Graphic novels are usually quality productions, sometimes run to hundreds of pages, and often cover serious subjects. Many Japanese manga focus on topics like the environment, the law, science, history – you name it.

Manga don't all look exactly the same, but they have some things in common:

Big Eyes

Oversized Expressions

Fast Action

Reading Manga:
How to Follow

Each page of a graphic novel is divided into boxes called panels. You follow the panels from left to right and top to bottom, like this:

Each panel is like a paragraph in a regular book. It shows you where the characters are, and what they are doing, saying and thinking.

Some panels include a little box at the top (or the bottom), giving you information about what's going on. These are called captions.

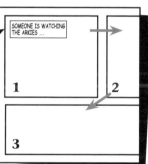

SOMEONE IS WATCHING THE ARKIES ...

DID YOU KNOW?

Traditional Japanese manga look a little different. That's because in Japan, people read from right to left. Japanese manga is read like this:

It's easier than it looks!

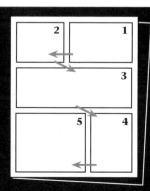

Reading Manga: Who's talking?

Speech balloons tell you who is speaking, what they're saying, and how.

Sometimes the lettering changes, to tell you which words are most important. These words might appear in **BOLD** or LARGE TYPE or in *ITALICS*.

Sometimes a punctuation point is enough to explain what's going on.

And how would you show an alien language? Maybe like this:

Reading Manga: What's that sound?

When you read speech bubbles, you hear manga characters' voices inside your head. There's a way to hear the background noises too – the rumble of thunder, the ringing of a telephone, the crack of a stick underfoot.

Manga artists represent sound effects (or SFX) by placing words over the panels, using lettering to suit each particular sound. It looks like this:

Scary sound

Mechanical sound

Quiet sound

DID YOU KNOW?

Japanese manga SFX are very precise. For example, *bicha bicha* means small splash, *bashan* is a medium splash, and *zaban* is a very big splash. There's even an SFX for total silence: *shiin*.

SFX are used to show emotions as well. The word *unzori* placed next to a character tells you they're feeling bored. If it was *moji moji* they'd be feeling shy, and *shobo shobo* indicates sadness.

Reading Manga:

What's that look on your Face?

Manga characters have exaggerated expressions, to help you understand what they're feeling. The first feature everyone notices is the eyes, which may be wide open in:

Shock

Fear

Hope

Closed eyes can mean:

Laughter

Sadness

Noses and chins are more difficult to spot (some characters have no nose at all). This reflects the Japanese preference for delicate features. In manga, big noses and chins are kept for the bad guys.

Reading Manga:

What's that look on your Face?

Just like manga characters' eyes, manga mouths are either huge or tiny. A big, wide-open mouth indicates:

Fear

Anger

Happiness

A character with a little mouth may be feeling:

Sad

Thoughtful

Shy

You can also tell a lot about manga characters from the crazy colour or style of their hair. For example, blue hair can mean the character is cool-headed, while orange hair equals determination (and sometimes a fiery temper). Wild, spiky hairstyles show the character is adventurous.

Three kinds of people live on Space Station Nova.

The Stationborn have been there for generations.

Jek

Prof

Zita

The Shipborn were born on giant spaceships that wander the Galaxy.

The Earthborn came to Nova from Earth.

Klikwitz

Mayor Gahdian

There has always been rivalry between the three sets of Stationers. But one thing might bring them together: the game they call 3D.

THE GREAT SPACE WANDERER, TARANTELLA, ROAMS THE GALAXY. ITS CREW, THE SHIPBORN, HAVE ALWAYS LIVED ON HER AND ALWAYS WILL ... OR SO THEY BELIEVE.

ON BOARD THE TARANTELLA, ZITA AND HER FATHER ARE SHARING A MEAL.

WHAT'S THE LETTER, DAD?

I'VE BEEN OFFERED A JOB.

I'LL BE ONE OF A NEW CREW AND GET TO BUILD NEW SYSTEMS, STREAMLINE OP—

WHAT'S THE CATCH?

THE CATCH IS, WE'LL BE MOVING TO SPACE STATION NOVA.

A SPACE STATION? YOU CAN'T BE SERIOUS. NOT GOING TO HAPPEN, DAD.

NO WAY!

- 10 -

MEANWHILE, ON SPACE STATION NOVA, PROF IS ALSO HAVING TROUBLE WITH HIS DAD.

C'MON, DAD, YOU SAID WE COULD HAVE A GAME IN THE DOME THIS TIME.

SORRY PROF. I DON'T HAVE TIME.

I HAVE TO FINISH THIS REPORT FOR MAYOR GAHDIAN'S NEW IMPROVEMENT PROJECT, AND THEN I'VE GOT TO PRACTISE.

MAYOR GAHDIAN'S 'IMPROVEMENTS' JUST MAKE THINGS WORSE.

WHY CAN'T HE LEAVE THINGS ALONE?

BECAUSE HE'S EARTHBORN, I EXPECT. HE MAY NOT UNDERSTAND HOW STATION SOCIETY WORKS.

KLIKWITZ, THE MAYOR'S NEPHEW, HAS A NEW TOY.

I'LL BE ABLE TO KEEP WATCH ON PEOPLE WITH THIS, UNCLE.

MAYOR G

ESPECIALLY THE SHIPBORN. WHEN'RE THEY COMING?

VERY SOON, KLIKWITZ. THEY'RE ON THEIR WAY.

GO AND PLAY WITH SOMEONE. HOW ABOUT DOC'S SON?

PROF HATES ME. HE'S MEAN.

OFF YOU GO.

DOC IS ON HIS WAY TO PRACTISE WITH THE 3D TEAM.

I'M RUNNING LATE, THANKS TO THE MAYOR.

3D IS THE BEST SPORT IN THE UNIVERSE.

THE BLUE TEAM CAPTAIN IS ANNOYED WITH DOC.

YOU'RE LATE – AGAIN!

BEEN TRAINING THAT BOY OF YOURS?

I WISH!

I BARELY HAVE TIME TO TRAIN MYSELF.

PROF AND HIS FRIEND, JEK, WATCH THE TEAM.

I DON'T KNOW HOW ANYONE CAN DO THAT, PROF.

IT'S EASY, ONCE YOU LEARN TO HANDLE THE LOW GRAVITY IN THE DOME.

YOU THINK SO?

I KNOW SO. I CAN DO THAT.

AND THAT. DAD'S TAUGHT ME ALL SORTS OF MOVES.

REALLY? WOW! I WISH—

- 15 -

- 16 -

PROF HAS SEEN ENOUGH.

HELP!

YOU TROD ON MY SPYGLASS! I'M GONNA TELL UNCLE!

THAT KID IS A MENACE.

YAHHHH HAAAAAAAA!

I'M GONNA TELL!

PROF AND JEK HELP ZITA TO HER FEET.

C'MON, KID. LET'S GET OUT OF HERE.

NO CHANCE NOW.

LET ME GO! I'VE GOT TO FIND DAD!

COME WITH US.

PROF INTRODUCES HIMSELF TO HIS GUEST.

I'M PROF, AND THIS IS JEK.

I AM ZITA TARANTELLA. WHY ARE YOU CALLED PROF?

IT'S SHORT FOR PROFESSOR, BECAUSE HE'S SO SMART.

WHAT SORT OF NAME IS TARANTELLA?

IT'S MY SHIP NAME.

WHAT'S THIS 3D THEN? DO YOU TWO PLAY IT?

OH NO! IT TAKES YEARS AND YEARS TO LEARN, AND WE'RE TOO YOUNG. PROF'S DAD PLAYS.

DAD IS THE BEST! HE'S TEACHING ME.

- 21 -

WHEN HE HAS TIME. AND THAT'S HARDLY EVER, BECAUSE—

SOMEONE IS EAVESDROPPING.

STORAGE

THE STUPID EARTHBORN MAYOR WON'T LEAVE HIM ALONE.

KLIKWITZ OVERHEARS WHAT PROF SAYS.

I KNEW HE WAS A MEAN BOY.

DAD WANTS ME TO HAVE A GOOD GROUNDING IN 3D BEFORE I TRY OUT FOR THE TEAM – WHEN I'M OLD ENOUGH.

LUCKY YOU! I WISH MY PARENTS COULD TEACH ME 3D.

DAD WOULD TEACH YOU IF THE MAYOR GAVE HIM SOME TIME.

HEY! IF DAD TRAINED YOU GUYS TOO, WE COULD HAVE A JUNIOR TEAM!

I WOULDN'T HAVE TO WAIT UNTIL I'M GROWN UP!

WE'D BE GROWN UP BEFORE WE LEARNED ENOUGH ANYHOW. EVERYONE KNOWS YOU HAVE TO TRAIN FOR YEARS.

ROF HAS NEWS FOR DOC.

THIS IS ZITA. SHE'S SHIPBORN. SHE WANTS TO LEARN TO PLAY 3D!

AND JEK WANTS TO LEARN TOO. WE COULD FIND SOMEONE ELSE AND HAVE A JUNIOR TEAM.

WAIT A MINUTE!

HOW DO YOU EXPECT TO DO THIS? I HOPE YOU DON'T THINK I CAN COACH YOU?

I BARELY HAVE TIME FOR MY OWN 3D PRACTICE WITH ALL THIS EXTRA WORK FOR THE MAYOR! IN FACT, I HAVE TO GO NOW.

MEANWHILE, MAYOR GAHDIAN IS ANGRY.

I HAVE BEEN TOLD BY A RELIABLE SOURCE THAT YOU ARE CRITICISING MY METHODS.

I HEARD HIM SAY IT, UNCLE.

I DON'T DENY IT. ARE YOU SURPRISED THE STATIONERS ARE ANGRY?

SHIPBORN OUT! SHIPBORN OUT!

WE DON'T HAVE ROOMS FOR ALL THE NEW PEOPLE, THE AIR SUPPLY WON'T LAST, THE—

IF YOU'RE SO CLEVER, YOU CAN SORT THIS OUT. YOU'RE NOW MY ASSISTANT.

IF PEOPLE THINK DOC'S IN CHARGE, THEY'LL BLAME HIM INSTEAD OF ME.

I REALLY WALKED INTO THAT ONE! I'LL JUST HAVE TO DO MY BEST.

- 29 -

Trouble on Nova
Nova Speak

3D A skilled ball game played on space stations.

Anchor-tatt A small anchor tattoo, found

on the hand of all Shipborn.

Dome A low-gravity cylinder with see-through

walls, where 3D is played.

Earthborn People born on Earth.

Holoplayers Holographic 3D players, used

to train teams.

Shipborn People born on huge spaceships.

Stationborn People born on big space

stations, like *Nova*.

Tarantella A spaceship. Zita's birthplace.